23:35

D1451829

Colin

Pam

Amrita

C Talk about the picture. What are the children doing? Where are they? **PH** Introduce short **a** sound as in **Amrita**. Let pupils give other words beginning with **a**. Practise Twister 1 (inside back cover). **WA** Have pupils match flashcards with **Colin**, **Pam**, **Amrita** to names on chalkboard (CB). **N** Have pupils count birds, books, chickens, trees, mangoes, pigs, pots (of plants), etc. Write the words on the CB. Let pupils write the appropriate numbers beside them.

1

Come and Look

Come, Amrita, come.
Come, Pam, come.
Come here.

Pam, Amrita, look!
Look here.
Look at this.

PH Introduce initial **l** sound as in **look**. Have pupils find (1) items in picture (pp. 2–3) beginning with **l**, e.g., **legs**, **lips**, **leaves**, **lines**, **limbs**, **louvres**, **laces** (on Colin's shoes); (2) other items beginning with **l**. Practise **l** in Twister 2. **C** Why is Colin pointing? Why does the chicken have no legs? **WA** Create sets of flashcards for **come**, **here**, **this**. Play matching game.

PH Introduce **p** as in **Pam**. Pupils find other words in the picture beginning with **p** sound, e.g., **plant**, **picture**, **page**, **post**, **pot**, **plait**. Practise **p** as in Twister 3. **C** What were Amrita and Pam doing when Colin called them? Look at the expression on Colin's face. How do you think he is feeling? Look at Pam and Amrita's faces. What are they thinking and feeling?

3

No, Colin!
Look here, Colin. Look!
Pam, Pam, come here!
Come, Pam. Look!
Look here. Look at this.

PH Introduce hard **c** as in **Colin** and **come**. Pupils point to capital and common **c**. Teams take turns giving words starting with hard **c** sound. E.g., Team One: **C** (say the sound, **not the name of the letter**) is for **car**. Team Two: **C** is for **cap**. Practise Twister 4. **C** Who tells Colin, "**No**"? Why? Why is Amrita so excited? What do you think is going to happen?

No, Amrita. No!
No, no, no!

PH Revise initial **a** sound as in **Amrita**. Ask pupils to think of other names beginning with **a** sound. What other words begin with **a** sound? **C** Why does Mummy shout "**No!**"? Why does the hen in the story say "**No, no, no!**"? Point out that hens don't talk, of course! What sound do they make? **A** Let pupils draw a picture of the hen and write their own speech balloon. **N** Have pupils count (1) the eggs, (2) the children, (3) the flowers in the picture.

Look, Amrita.
Look, Pam.
Look, Colin.
Look at this.

PH Revise **p** and **l** sounds as in **Pam** and **Look**. Play word game as on page 4 to practise **p** and **l**. **C** Talk about various animals and their young. Which ones come from eggs? **N** How many eggs are there? How many have hatched? How many children are there? How many flowers are there? **N & A** Pupils draw three of anything and label with numeral 3.

The Mango

Come, Amrita. Come, Pam.
Come here and look.
Look at this.

7

What is it, Colin?
What is it? What is it?

A mango! A mango!
Look at this mango!

PH Revise initial **a** as in **a**, **at** (p. 8) and **and** (p. 9). Practise **a** in Twister 1. Revise initial **l** as in **look**. Have pupils put **a** and **l** sounds together to make **Al**. Use flashcards with **a**, **l** and **p** to make **Al** and **pal**. LP Ask questions using the verb **is**, e.g., Where is Colin? What is he doing? Is he safe? Where is Amrita? Pupils answer individually in complete sentences. C Talk about climbing: Do pupils climb? Is it safe?

A mango! A mango!
Where, Colin? Where?

Look up here.
The mango is up here.
I have the mango.
I have it.

Look, Tim, a mango.

Look, Tom, a mango.

9

No, Colin.
You do not have it.
Look. I have the mango.
I have it. I have it.

Look, Tom!
A mango

Look, Tim!
A mango

PH Practise **h** sound as in Twister 7. **LP** Talk about the pronoun **I**. Point out that it is always a capital letter. Use **I** in language drill, e.g., *Teacher:* I have the mango. *Pupils:* I have the mango. *Teacher:* orange *Pupils:* I have the orange. Use **plum**, **cherry**, etc., to continue drill. **A** Work with groups to make up simple twisters that practise **h** sound. **C** Who says, "**No, Colin.**" Why does she say it?

Oh no, Colin!
Look! Look!
The pigs! The pigs!

No, Amrita, not the pigs.
I have it, not the pigs.
Look, Pam. I have it.
I have the mango.

PH Introduce initial **t** sound as in **Tom** and **Tim**. Practise **t** and plurals in Twister 9. Pupils give other words beginning with **t**. **C** How do you think the children are feeling? What about the pigs? How did the pigs get out? How can the children stop the pigs getting out again? Talk about what pigs eat. Do they eat mangoes? **A** Pupils make up what happens next in the story. Does Colin eat the mango? Does he give it to Mummy? Do the pigs get some?

This is for You

Here, Amrita. This is for you.
Come, Pam. This is for you.
This is for you.
This is for me.

And this is for me!

PH Practise **f** sound as in **for**. Practise Twister 10. Find items on the page beginning with **f** sound, e.g., **foot**, **forehead**.
LP Let pupils act out the sharing of the mango, saying each time, "**This is for you**". Emphasize the sound of **th** as in **this**. **C** What do you think the mongoose will do? Look at Mummy. Why do you think she has a knife in her hand? Why is she smaller than Colin, Pam and Amrita?

See. This is for you, Amrita.
This is for you, Pam.
This is for me.

And this is for Sam.
I am Sam.

C Look closely at Colin's plate. What is happening? How many pieces will Colin have at the end? PH Introduce s as in see and Sam. Practise s sound in Twister 11. Revise a in am and Amrita. Point out rhyming words am, Pam, Sam. WA Use flashcards with p, a, m, s to make am, Pam, Sam. Pupils use flashcards with p, a, m, s to make as many words as they can.

This is for you, Amrita.
This is for you, Pam.
This is for me.

And this is for me, Sam.

C How do you think Colin will feel when he finds out what is happening to his share of the mango? What do you think he will do? What would you do? PH Revise f as in for. Have pupils practise f sound in Twisters 10 and 12. WA Revise adding -s to show more than one (p. 11), as in mongoose +s = mongooses. A Talk about mongooses. Let pupils give all the information they have on mongooses. What do they eat? (Most eat chickens, snakes, rats, insects, worms, but some eat fruit.)

Pam! Amrita! My mango is not here!
Where is it? Where is it?
Where is my mango?

PH Revise **m** sound. Practise Twister 6. **LP** Use the word **where** in a question and answer drill, to practise the use of the question form, Where is…? E.g., *Teacher:* Where is the mongoose? *Pupils:* Where is the mongoose? *Teacher:* mango *Pupils:* Where is the mango? *Teacher:* man *Pupils:* Where is the man? Use words beginning with **m**, e.g., **mop**, **mat**, **mask**, **money**, **moon**, **milk**, etc., to continue drill.

Oh no!
My mango!

My mango!

C Who has Colin's mango? What do you think will happen next? Why do you think the mongoose hasn't started eating his mango yet? When do you think he is going to eat it? What do you think of this mongoose? Is he badly behaved? Mischievous? A trickster? **PH** Introduce **n** sound as in **not** (p. 16) and **no** (p. 17). Practise **n** in Twister 13. Revise word families **am**, **Pam**, **Sam**; **Al**, **pal**, **Sal**. **A** Pupils use **I** with **am**, **Pam**, **Sam**, **Al**, **pal**, **Sal** to make simple poem.

17

Look, Colin. Have this.
Yes, Colin. Have this.
Have a bit of my mango.

Thank you, Amrita.
Thank you, Pam.
Thank you for the mango.

Thank you, Colin.

PH Revise **h** sound as in **have**. Practise Twister 7. **C & N** How many pieces did Colin cut the mango into? How many did Amrita and Pam each have on their plates? How many did Colin have? Why do Amrita and Pam give Colin some of their mango? How many pieces does Colin get in the end? How does Colin feel now? Would you do what Pam and Amrita did? Why/Why not? **A** Talk about the story of Anancy and the bananas. Is Colin like Anancy? Why/Why not?

Get Out! Get Out!

Where is the mongoose?
Is it in here, Pam?

No, not in here, Colin.

PH Introduce hard **g** as in **get**. Practise **g** in Twister 14. Pupils find items beginning with **g** sound on the page, e.g., **ground**, **girl**, **grass**. C Use the next four pages as a sequencing activity to give pupils a sense of the unfolding story. Discuss the clues given about the mongoose's movement. Where is he coming from? Where is he going? Why can't the children find him?

Where is the mongoose?
Is it in here, Amrita?

No, not in here, Colin.

20   **C** Why do you think the children want to find the mongoose? Why can't they catch him? **PH** Talk about the difference between **o** in **no** and **o** in **not**. Have pupils give words to rhyme with **no** and words to rhyme with **not**. Practise these in Twisters 15 and 16. **LP** Use drill to practise Is it...? No, it is not... *Teacher:* Is it in your bag? *1st pupil:* No it is not in my bag. *1st pupil to next pupil:* Is it in your bag? And so on.

Where is the mongoose?
Where is it?

Is it in here, Colin?
Is the mongoose in here, Colin?
Is it in here?

PH Introduce **i** sound as in **is**, **it** and **in**. Practise Twister 17. Use **i**, **t**, **n**, **s** and **f** on flashcards to build **it**, **in**, **is**, **if**.
C Can you see the mongoose now? How do you know where he is? What will the children do next? Have pupils take up positions **in**, **on**, **under**, **beside** using furniture and places in the classroom, e.g., chair, desk, window, doorway. Talk about the difference between **in**, **on**, **under** and **beside**.

21

In here!
Oh no, Pam.
Oh no, Amrita.

Not in here!
Get out, mongoose.
Get out!
Get out!
Get out!

22 **PH** Revise hard **g** as in **get**. Revise **o** as in **Oh** and **no**. Introduce medial **o** as in **not**. Build word family **not**, **got**, **lot**, **cot**, **pot**. **P** Talk about full stops and exclamation marks. What do exclamation marks mean? Why is the last **"Get out!"** in dark lettering (boldface)? **C** What do you think the children would do if they caught the mongoose? **A** Pupils tell stories they know or make up about animals. Give each pupil a turn.

Read for Fun

What is that?

That is a hat on a mat.

What is that?

That is a cat on a mat.

That is a cat under a hat.

What is that?

That is a rat beside the hat.

PH Introduce **r** as in **rat**. What other animals' names begin with **r** sound? E.g., **rooster**, **rabbit**, **ram**, **raccoon**. Make flashcards with letters **c, p, s, h, m, f, r** to use with **-at** to build word family. Practise **r** as in Twister 18. Revise **in, on, under, beside**. **LP** Use drill to practise What is that? That is… *Teacher:* What is that? That is a hat. *Pupils:* That is a hat. *Teacher:* rat What is that? *Pupils:* That is a rat. Continue drill with **bat, cat, mat, ham**. Repeat cues as necessary.

23

What is that?

That is a cat on a mat.

That is a cat under a hat.

That is a rat beside a cat.

What is that?

That is a cat under a hat on a mat.

Where is the rat?

PH Revise **c, h, r, m**. Let each pupil write a word beginning with one of these letters. Put **c, h, r, m** headings on CB. Have pupils put their words under the right heading. **LP & N** Practise plurals and counting by saying Twister 19. **C** What happens to the rat in the picture? Why are there no rats at the end of Twister 19?

Why Do You Want a Pin?

Come, Colin. Come, Pam and Andy.
We are going to the sea.
We are going in the car.

PH Introduce **w** sound as in **we**. Practise Twister 20. Revise **t** as in **to**. **LP** *Teacher:* We are going to the sea. *Pupils:* We are going to the sea. *Teacher:* shop *Pupils:* We are going to the shop. *Teacher:* zoo *Pupils:* We are going to the zoo. Use other cues like **airport**, **movies**, **museum**, **library** to continue drill. **C** Is Daddy going to the beach too? How can you tell?

Mummy, do you have a big pin?

Yes, I have a big pin.
What are you going to do with a pin?

PH Introduce **b** sound as in **big**. Practise Twister 21. Pupils find items on pages 26–27 beginning with **b** sound, e.g., **box**, **bucket**, **bananas**, **basket**, **ball**, **bed**, **book**, etc. **C** Where will Mummy find a pin? Why do you think the pin is there? What kind of pin does Colin want?

Pam, do you have some string?

Yes, I have some string.
What do you want to do with some string?

C What do you think Colin wants the string for? Where will he find string? What do you think Pam is going to do with the bucket and the pillow? What is Andy going to do with the ball? **PH** Revise w sound as in **want** and **with**. Practise Twister 20. **LP** Use drill to practise Do you have…? Yes, I have… *Teacher*: Do you have a pin? Yes, I have a pin. *Pupils*: Yes, I have a pin. *Teacher*: Do you have a stick? *Pupils*: Yes, I have a stick. Continue drill with **hook**, **ball**, **worm**, etc.

Daddy, can you get a stick?

Yes, I can get a stick.
What are you going to do with a stick?

PH Introduce initial **d** as in **Daddy** and **do**. Pupils give other words beginning with **d** sound. Practise **d** in Twister 22.
C Where will Daddy get a stick? Will it be big or small? Straight or curved? Do you think it matters? **A** Talk about different ways of catching fish, e.g., with a small net, a fishing rod, a spear, a seine (a very large fishing net).

Daddy, can you get a worm?

Yes, I can get a worm.
What do you want to do with a worm?

I want to put the worm on the pin.
I want to put the pin on the string.
I want to put the string on the stick.

PH Revise **s** as in **sea** and **stick**. Practise Twister 11. Talk about **th** as in **the**. Point out that **th**, as in **the**, is different from **th**, as in **think**. Use the story on pages 23–24 to practise **th**, as in **the** and **that**. **LP** *Teacher:* I want to put the pen on the table. *Pupils:* I want to put the pen on the table. *Teacher:* box *Pupils:* I want to put the box on the table. *Teacher:* ball *Pupils:* I want to put the ball on the table. **C** What is Daddy doing with the stick? Why?

29

And what are you going to do with the pin and the string and the stick and the worm?

You will see, Pam and Andy.
You will see. You will see.

PH Revise **a** as in **and** and **Andy**. Introduce medial **a** as in **Pam** (p. 30) and **mat**, **has** and **mangoes** (p. 31). Practise medial **a** in Twister 23. **C** Do you think Pam knows what Colin is going to do? Do you think Andy knows what Colin is going to do? Why is Colin smiling? **A** Prepare cards with the words **going**, **have**, **mango**, **sea**, **some**, **string**, **stick**, **worm**, **what**, **want**, **with**, **will**. Divide the class into groups and play Word Bingo.

Mummy, let us go. Pam has the mat.
Andy has the mangoes.
Colin has the stick with the pin
and the string and the worm.
Let us get into the car.
We are going to the sea.

C What do you think Pam is going to do with the mat at the beach? Why is the trunk of the car open? Do you think Andy is going to put the mangoes in the trunk? Why? Why not? LP Have individual pupils mime different activities at the beach (one at a time), e.g., **fishing**, **swimming**, **digging in the sand**, etc. *Pupil*: What am I doing? *Class*: You are swimming, you are fishing, etc.

Well, Colin, you have a pin.
You have some string.
You have a stick.
You have a worm.
Now you can fish.

Do you have a fish?

C What kind of fish do you think Colin will catch? Do you think they will be big or small fish? Why? Do you think they will take them home or cook them and eat them on the beach? What kinds of food do you think they have in the basket? **PH** Revise **f** sound as in **fish**. Practise **f** as in Twisters 10 and 12. **A** Pupils write a poem about a day at the beach using words from the text.

Read for Fun

Daddy! Look! Lo_o_k at my sti̯ck.
I have a string _n my st_ck.

L_ _k, Mummy. Look! Look _t the
h_ _k on the string on my stick!

L_ _k, Andy. Look!
The pin is a h_ _k. The p_n is the
h_ _k on the str_ng _n my st_ck.

Pam, l_ _k _t the worm,
the worm on the pin
on the string on my stick.

The f_sh has the worm!
I have the fish.

PH Have pupils fill in blanks on the page. Use words on this page to build word families, e.g., **look, cook, book, hook; fish, wish, dish; at, mat, cat, sat, rat, fat, hat, pat; pin, sin, fin, din.** Let pupils listen for medial **i** in **-ish** and **-in** families. Let pupils find items in picture beginning with **w** as in **wave, water, worm, wall**, etc. Revise **w** sound in Twister 20. **A** Use bingo cards and flashcards with words ending in **-ook, -ish, -st** and **-in** to play Word Bingo.

We Want to Play Football

Tom, you take this ball.
Let us go and play football.

34 **PH** Revise **b** sound sound as in **ball**, **boys**, **boots**. Have pupils use flashcards to label things in the classroom beginning with **b**, e.g., **book**, **bag**, **blackboard**, **boys**, **bench**, etc. Practise **b** in Twisters 21 and 24. **C** Talk about football. Is it a popular sport? Is there more than one kind of football? If so, talk about the various kinds. Can girls play football?

Can we come, Eric? Can we come?
We want to come with you.
We want to play football.

No, Amrita. No, Pam.
You cannot come.
We are going to play football.
Girls cannot play football.
You cannot come.

35

Come, Pam. Come, Carol and Sandra.

Let us go and play.

We can take some mangoes.

Girls **can** eat mangoes.

Look, Amrita. Look!

The boys are not playing.

They are beside Mr Brown's house.

They are looking under it.

PH Revise **th** as in **the** and **they**. Remind pupils that it is different from **th** in **think**. Pupils give other words beginning with **th** as in **think**, e.g., **thing**, **thin**, **thimble**, etc. Practise identifying final consonant **t** as in **let**, **it** and **eat**. Ask pupils to repeat the words until they can hear the final **t** sound. Pupils give other words that end with **t** sound. Practise final **t** in words on pages 22–24. **C** How do you think the girls feel about not being allowed to play football?

Hi, Colin. Hi, Tom. Hi, Eric.
Why are you looking under the house?
What are you looking for?

We are looking for the football.
It is under the house.
Eric cannot get under the house.
He is big.

PH Revise **h** sound as in **Hi**, **house** and **he**. Practise Twister 7. **C** How did the football get under the house? Revise the difference between **in**, **on**, **under** and **beside**. Have pupils take up positions **in**, **on**, **under**, **beside**, using furniture and places in the classroom. **LP** *Teacher*: We are looking for the football. *Pupils*: We are looking for the football. *Teacher*: net *Pupils*: We are looking for the net. Continue drill with cues like **bat**, **pen**, **bag**, **mangoes**, etc.

I will go, Eric.

I can get under the house.

I can get the ball.

Let me go.

No, Tom. You cannot go. You are too big.

You cannot get under the house.

You go, Colin. You are small.

You can get under the house.

PH Revise hard **c** as in **Colin** and **can**. Practise Twister 4. **C** Talk about final **g** as in **big**. Have pupils think of other words that end in **g** sound, e.g., **hog**, **bag**, **rug**, **leg**. Build word family **big**, **pig**, **wig**, **jig**. Practise Twister 25. **C** Talk about materials used to make houses, e.g., bricks, wood, cement, stones. What kind of house is the football stuck under? Who offers to go under the house? Who tells him that he cannot go?

Go under, Colin. Go under.
Go under the house.
Get the ball.
Can you see the ball?

No. I cannot see the ball
and I cannot come out.

PH Revise medial **o** as in **Colin** and **cannot**. Point out the difference between the medial **o** sound and the **o** sound in **no** and **go**. Practise Twister 25. **C** What has happened to Colin? What do you think the children will do? **A** Let pupils act out the section of the story on pages 38–39. Choose children to play the girls' as well as boys' parts. Encourage the girls to respond, even though they have no words to speak.

Oh no! What are we going to do?
Colin cannot see the ball and
he cannot come out from under the house.

Let me go, Eric.
I will go under the house.
I can push Colin out and
I will look for the ball.

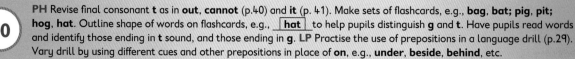

PH Revise final consonant **t** as in **out**, **cannot** (p.40) and **it** (p. 41). Make sets of flashcards, e.g., **bag, bat; pig, pit; hog, hat**. Outline shape of words on flashcards, e.g., ‗hat‗ to help pupils distinguish **g** and **t**. Have pupils read words and identify those ending in **t** sound, and those ending in **g**. **LP** Practise the use of prepositions in a language drill (p.29). Vary drill by using different cues and other prepositions in place of **on**, e.g., **under**, **beside**, **behind**, etc.

Push, Amrita, push. We can see Colin.
He is coming out.
Come out, Colin.

Where is the ball?
We cannot see it.
Do you have the ball, Colin?

PH Revise initial **i** as in **it** and **is**. Revise **i** In Twister 17. Introduce final consonant **n** as in **Colin**. Use **-in** to build word family: **in**, **bin**, **din**, **fin**, **pin**, **sin**, **win**. **C** Who do you think has the ball? Which way will Amrita come out from under the house? What do you think will happen next? Do drill to practise "Do you have … ?" *Teacher:* Do you have the ball? *Pupils:* Do you have the ball? *Teacher:* bat *Pupils:* Do you have the bat? Continue drill with **net**, **book**, **bat**, etc.

Pam, Sandra, come, come.
Come, Carol. I have the ball.
Girls **can** play football.
Let us play football.
Do you boys want to play?

PH Introduce medial vowel **e** as in **let**. Use **-et** to build word family: **bet**, **get**, **let**, **net**, **met**, **set**, **wet**. Have pupils practise medial **e**, and initial **th** in Twister 26. Use twister also to practise final **t** sound. **C** Will the boys play with the girls now? How many players will there be in each team? Look at the faces of the children in the picture. How do you think each child is feeling?

As Fast as We Can

I do not want to run.
I will come last.
I cannot run fast.
I do not want to go to sports
at school on Friday.

WA Use flashcard to introduce **sports** as sight word. **PH** Revise medial vowel **i** as in **will**. What other words have this sound in the middle? (See pp. 38 and 41.) Practise medial **i** as in Twister 27. **LP** Use drill to practise Do you want…? No, I do not want… *Teacher*: Do you want a pin? No, I do not want a pin. *Pupils*: No, I do not want a pin. *Teacher*: Do you want a stick? *Pupils*: No, I do not want a stick. Continue drill with **hook**, **ball**, **worm**, etc.

Come, Colin, come.
Run to Mummy.
She is at the bus stop.
She has a bad foot.
We have to help.
We have to get Daddy.

Daddy is at the shop with Andy.
We have to run as fast as we can.
Come, Colin. Run!

PH Talk about **u** sound in the middle of **bus** and **run**. Use **-un** to build word family: **run**, **sun**, **fun**, **bun**, **nun**. Practise medial **u** in Twister 28. **LP** Have pupils talk about the pictures on pages 44–45 to practise the present continuous tense. Ask them to look at the pictures and say what each one is doing, e.g., The man is driving. Daddy is buying groceries, etc. If you wish, do this as a drill: *Teacher:* What are Colin and Pam doing? *Pupil:* They are running to find Daddy. *Teacher:* What is Daddy doing? etc.

Look, Daddy, look!
Look at Colin and Pam.
They are running.
Colin is running fast.
He is running as fast as
he can.

Daddy, Daddy! Mummy has a bad foot.
She is at the bus stop.
She wants you to come in the car.
She wants you to come as fast as you can.
Oh! Hi, Mr Green.
Hi, Colin.

Mummy has a bad foot! Oh no!
Come, Daddy, let us go.
Let us get into the car.
We have to go as fast as we can.

C Why does everyone have to go as fast as they can? How is Mummy feeling? How do you think she hurt her foot?
PH Talk about **sh** as in **she** (p. 46) and **shop** (p. 44). Pupils give other words beginning with **sh** sound. Practise initial
sh in Twister 30. LP Practise **has** in a drill. *Teacher:* Mummy has a good friend. *Pupils:* Mummy has a good friend.
Teacher: Grandma *Pupils:* Grandma has a good friend. Continue drill with other nouns and pronouns (**he, she**) as cues.

Colin, you take the fish.

Pam, you take the mangoes.

Andy, you can take my hat.

Let us get into the car.

Let us go to the bus stop to get Mummy.

Let us go as fast as we can.

We are going to take Mummy home.

PH Revise medial **o** sound as in **stop** and **shop**. Pupils say other words with this sound in the middle. Practise Twister 31. **C** How does Daddy manage to get the groceries into the car so fast? **LP** *Teacher*: Let us go to the shop. *Pupils*: Let us go to the shop. *Teacher*: to the sea *Pupils*: Let us go to the sea. *Teacher*: to the ship *Pupils*: Let us go to the ship. Continue drill with other cues.

Hello, Daddy. Hello, Andy.
Hi, Colin and Pam. Thank you.
You can run, Pam.
You can run fast.

I can win.

No, Mummy.
I cannot run as fast as Colin.
He can win at sports on Friday.
Yes, Daddy. Colin can run fast!
He can win.

PH Revise initial **d** as in **Daddy**. Ask pupils to listen for all the **d** sounds in **Daddy**, **Andy** and **Friday**. Talk about where they occur. Have pupils give other words with **d** (1) at the beginning, (2) in the middle. **C** Do you think Colin will run on sports day? Do you think he will win the races? Do you like sports day? Which is your favourite race?
A Draw pictures of sports day. Pupils write their names on their pictures. Make a classroom display.